P9-CKS-294

Galápagos bedtime stories

by Paula Tagle Saad

ISBN 9978-43-508-5

Glossary source The Oxford Dictionary of Natural History, 1985
Edited by Michael Allaby
Foreword by David Attenborough

Illustration: Rolando Portero

Graphic design: Carlos Alberto Andrade

To the memory of the woman who wrote a book for me, to teach me to read, Isabel Herrería Herrería, my grandmother.
When one keeps the memory of a beloved person present, their essence will always live.

index

acknowledgments

When I visited the Galápagos Islands as a teenager, the innocence of its creatures and the amazing geology bewitched me, so in 1992 I became a naturalist guide for the Galápagos National Park. Here I found the "Never, Never Land" I had longed for since I was a child. This archipelago hasn't remained completely isolated from world problems, but it is still one of the most pristine places on earth, where conservationist attitudes and efforts are a reality.

I got the idea for this book when Aisha, my eight-year old niece, visited me on board the MS Polaris. Every evening I recapitulated the experiences of the day, but in the form of short stories so she and I could have more fun and still learn. That was the beginning of "Galápagos Bedtime Stories". My hope is that before going to sleep, people of all ages will remember a bit about the island that they just visited through the characters in the tales. Thanks Aisha for inspiring the idea!

I wish to thank my two old good friends Cindy Manning and Paul McFarling for patiently reading the stories and saving me from making mistakes in the English language. Cindy with her US English, and Paul with his British viewpoint, have given my book a "balanced" English, that will be understood by everyone.

Steve Ewing gave the final touch to the English grammar, and Carlos Alberto Andrade worked on the graphic design of the book, therefore they both deserve particular thanks.

I also want to thank each and every one of the naturalists with whom I have sailed during my time in Galápagos. It has been an extraordinary privilege. I have learned from each of them, in every outing, in every talk, with every drink. They are all my colleagues and my mentors.

For my training in Galápagos and for the confidence that I received during my early years as a naturalist I am eternally grateful to Metropolitan Touring, ETICA, and their people.

Special thanks to Lindblad Expeditions, not only for these many years of prime expeditions aboard its ships, or for the wonderful library and the many opportunities to expand my knowledge, but also for the great support to the conservation of the Galápagos Islands. I am very proud to be part of a company that promotes and gives so much to the preservation of this unique place in the world.

Many thanks to the crews with whom I have worked in Galápagos. They are people with eagle eyes and great hearts! And of course to the officers and crew of the MS Polaris for these seven years of good work.

I have a special appreciation for my friends, Doctor José “Saudade” Machuca and Desirèe Cruz, for their encouragement to write, and for their letters that kept me in touch with my beloved islands during the years I was away.

To my parents, Juan and Isabel, and to my uncle, Pedro Saad, my gratitude for reading and commenting on the different stories and characters. For the spirit of writing!

Many thanks to Daniel Sanchez, for his endless patience and unconditional support.

And thanks to you all, visitors to the Galápagos, because you are our best ambassadors to the world.

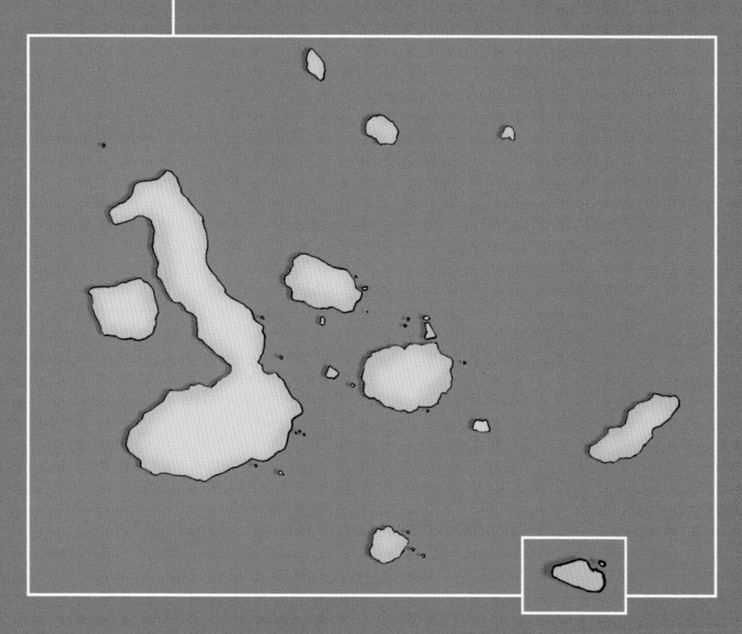

Wavy, The albatross that was afraid of heights

Española bedtime story

One wonderful May morning, an albatross' egg hatched. Its father, proud and fulfilled, smiled at the cliffs of Española Island.

The baby was a tiny brown ball of downy feathers. Nutty gulls laughed at the helpless chick, but his father was too happy with his very first hatchling to pay attention to them.

Wavy was the name of this newborn chick of Española Island.

"I wish Mom would come back soon to feed our baby," thought the father. "She will bring juicy oil to our little one, and then I will be able to go myself to fish for our Wavy."

They had to wait 2 days until Mom came back. In the mean time, Father told Wavy about the far places albatrosses go to fish. They fly miles away from shore, which is why it takes them so long to come back. But they always manage to return, and always to Española. This is the only place in the world where waved albatrosses nest. With their great sense of smell, they find their way back to their homes and families.

When Mom Albatross finally arrived, the sight of her chick already walking around pleasantly surprised her. Wavy was really hungry, so Mom immediately regurgitated a juicy oil, with fresh calamari aroma. She had prepared this great meal herself by mixing (in her stomach) all the different flavors of the squid and fish she had eaten during her days at sea.

As Wavy was growing up unduly fast, both parents went to fish together. They did not need to worry about predators for Wavy. Española was extremely safe. Humans hadn't introduced any of those big mammals from the mainland, and the sole natural predator was the Galápagos hawk. But Wavy was too big and heavy for such a little bird of prey.

So Wavy was left alone for many days in a row. However, he never felt lonesome. He made a good friend, Don Hood Cucuve, one small and noisy mockingbird.

"You know something Wavy? We, the mockingbirds, are even more important than those minuscule Darwin's finches. Did you know that Darwin noticed us first, we were his inspiration!"

"Did you know, Wavy, that we are both notably unique birds? Yeah! You look big, I am tiny, however we have a lot in common…we are both endemic! Unique to Española, found nowhere else in the world."

That's how they both spent long hours at the westernmost point of Española Island. Their favorite hobby was to shower under the "rainbow water" coming from the blowhole. They walked to the very edge of the southern cliffs when the tide was coming in. They waited for the biggest wave to hit the crack in the lava, counted to three and opened their wings. It was great to feel that strong spray of sea all over them! And sometimes the tiny droplets of water split the light into a wonderful rainbow, so it became their rainbow shower. They also loved to watch sunsets.

Many days would pass before one of Wavy's parents would come back with food. Hence, Don Hood Cucuve was the only company that the chick had while growing up.

The mockingbird always brought him news about the rest of the island.

"You know, Wavy, there are many newborn sea lions on the northern beach, and sometimes they are so awfully loud babies, it is unbearable!"

"You know, Wavy, one day you will be gone from Española, and you will be gone for a long time, five years or more. By then you will have forgotten me."

"I will never forget you my dear friend!" said Wavy.

"You albatrosses all behave that way," replied Don Hood Cucuve. "You disappear until you feel ready to find a mate, and only then do you come back to Española. And you are such romantic creatures that once you find a spouse, it is forever, together to the end of your lives!"

Don Hood Cucuve had many brothers and sisters, but of them all, he preferred to share his time with Wavy. One day, the mockingbird realized that Wavy was getting overly big, and that he was not yet showing any interest in flight. So Don Hood Cucuve decided to take Wavy to Albatross Airport. He could learn to fly by seeing the other albatrosses taking off from the cliffs.

"You should watch those guys carefully. See the way they open their wings, how they face the wind and wait its right speed and direction. You will become a great pilot, but you must watch the experts first."

"I will never make it! I am afraid of heights!" was Wavy's response.

"You will make it. You simply need to lose weight. You'll have to go on a diet. See the way the albatrosses run!"

One afternoon Wavy's mom gave him a big kiss and told him she was not going to be able to return. The ocean around Galápagos was warming up, and it was becoming extremely difficult to find food. Wavy looked almost ready to fly, and she would wait for him, far at sea, together with the other albatrosses. Wavy's father did not come back either. It was just the island, a few single albatrosses still around, and Don Hood Cucuve.

Wavy began to lose weight. He was so hungry that his good friend, worried about Wavy's health, brought him flies and leaves. But albatrosses are not mockingbirds, they are sea birds, and Wavy missed his parents' great smashed squid.

Don Hood Cucuve put him on a strong fitness workout. Wavy had to jog along the cliff, early in the morning, then he had to watch the other albatrosses taking off. Finally he had to exercise his wings for two hours. The training ended in a great rainbow shower at the blowhole, and with a nice long conversation about the open seas, while watching the sunset.

"Why can't I be a land bird like you are, dear Don Hood Cucuve?" asked Wavy.

"Do not complain Wavy! You can go much further than I can. I am not even able to leave this island, yet you will see the world. You will get down to the seas along the Peruvian and Ecuadorian coast."

"I don't want to see the world. I just want to stay with you," cried Wavy.

The mockingbird was getting worried. It was time for his timid and afraid-of-heights friend to fly and depart. The last albatrosses were leaving the island, and they were going to be away for at least 3 months, as long as the warm rainy season lasted. There was no choice. Wavy had to leave too. For that reason the mockingbird made a hard decision. He was going to push Wavy off the cliff. Wavy had all the feathers Albatrosses require for flying. He was ready, and he just needed a push.

So Don Hood Cucuve, hiding his real intentions, brought Wavy to the airport. They watched the last adult albatross taking off. Then, without warning, the mockingbird disappeared.

"Where are you dear friend?" called Wavy.

Within seconds Don Hood Cucuve was below Wavy's wing, softly pecking at the wavy feather pattern under his wings, from where they got the name of "waved" albatrosses. Then the mockingbird moved to Wavy's feet, tickling, making Wavy laugh and laugh. He couldn't stop laughing and moving all over. Finally Wavy lost his balance, and in the middle of a great chuckle, stumbled over the cliff.

Don Hood Cucuve watched him fall. His heart stopped beating for seconds that seemed an eternity. His friend was going down toward the rocks and the rough seas.

"He's not going to make it! What have I done?" cried Don Hood Cucuve.

But then, Wavy instinctively opened his wings, faced the southern trade winds, and got the lift he needed to go up and up. He suddenly looked like a different creature. He was not the helpless albatross chick anymore. In the blink of an eye, he had become a majestic bird. Until that moment, Don Hood Cucuve hadn't realized how big his friend actually was. His wings were colossal; eight-foot wings all spread out to the breeze.

The ocean was blue and the skies were blue. The tide was coming in, and the blowhole looked more powerful than ever, spouting a wonderful rainbow shower. Wavy was going around and around without even flapping his wings! He played with air currents and enjoyed the flight, as if he had been born doing it. He was a great glider, a wonderful example of a waved albatross, one of the largest seabirds in the world.

Wavy tried to land to say farewell to Don Hood Cucuve, though he was traveling too fast to stop. He knew that most of the albatross's accidents occurred during landing. He had no other choice than to wave goodbye to his friend from the air, and dipped his wings in salute as he passed low. Then he headed south, to meet others of his kind.

Don Hood Cucuve watched him disappear over the horizon. A perfect flying machine designed for long, extremely long flights.

Don Hood Cucuve missed Wavy for many years; the sunsets had lost their meaning, as well as the rainbow showers. Five years passed by until one May morning Don Hood Cucuve felt a touch on his shoulder.

He turned around and met a wonderful full-grown albatross, dressed in pure white with a bright orange beak and huge eyes. It was Wavy!

"Hello old friend! Why don't we take a bath at the blowhole, one big rainbow shower?"

Wavy had come back! It was that same naïve voice and broad smile! Don Hood Cucuve's friend hadn't forgotten him and hadn't forgotten their unique home island.

After cooling off in the blowhole's refreshing waters, Wavy invited Don Hood Cucuve to the albatross airport cliff.

"Do you see that tiny brown ball of downy feathers at the edge? That is my little Wavy. Would you like to teach him all that you taught me years ago? You are a great pilot instructor, but above all, a great friend," said Big Wavy.

Don Hood Cucuve's chest puffed up with pride. It was a big honor to become the tutor of such a majestic species. However, he felt happier rather than proud. He had a new friend, a new Wavy with whom to share the rainbow showers of Española Island.

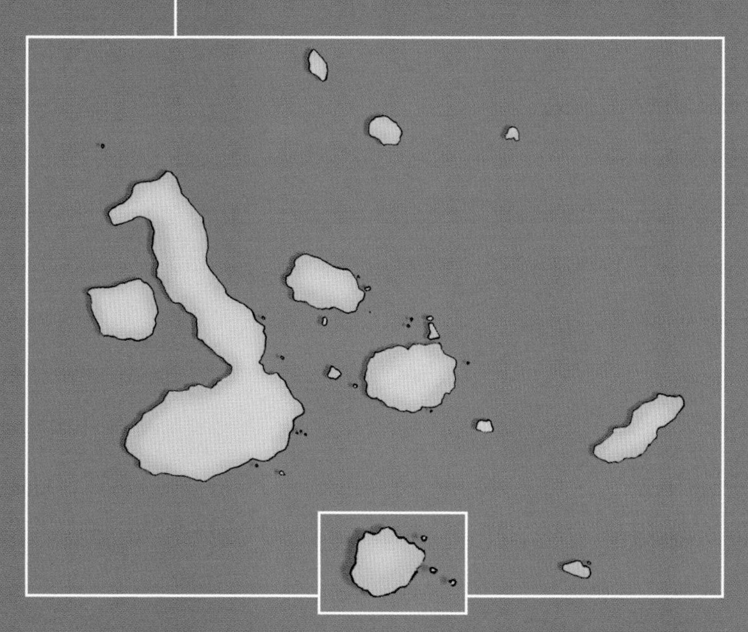

The meeting of the wisest

Floreana bedtime story

The meeting of the wisest animals took place on Floreana Island, one early morning in the dry-cool season, known as the "Garua" season. The entire Island smelled like the Galápagos incense tree, the "Palo Santo", and was painted in "Palo Santo" colors as well. It looked white and pink, like the bark of this tree that sleeps for most of the year.

At the "flour" beach of Punta Cormorant, located on the northernmost point of Floreana, the wisest of all the creatures of Galápagos met to solve a long-thought mystery. Why was the sand of the eastern beach of Punta Cormorant so white and fine, when green-black grains made up the western beach?

The wisest from the sea as well as the wisest from the land were invited, and the reunion was at a convenient place to everyone: the charming piece of driftwood, half in the water, and half on land on this flour beach. The huge balsa log faced the turquoise water, the habitat of the wisest from the sea, and was surrounded by white sand, a good site for the wisest from the land. Mr. Pink Flamingo led the convention.

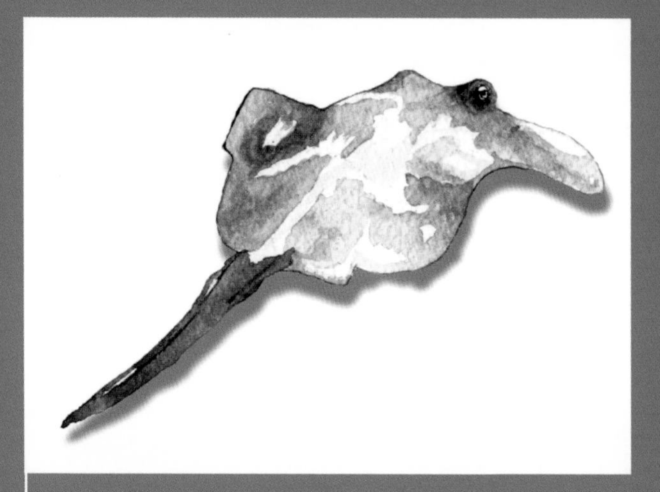

"We are reunited here to discuss a great mystery. To solve a question that has been in our minds since the very beginning. Why is it that the sand on this beach is so different from the sand on the other side? Does anyone have an idea?"

The diamond stingray, who lives in the shallow waters of the beach, raised her fin to speak her opinion.

"This is very fine sand because of us, the marvelous sting rays. For many years we have burrowed into this sand in search of crustaceans, our main food. Slowly but surely, we pulverized the grains with our mouth plates, and we have squeezed the color out of them, hence producing a pure white beach."

The ghost crab interrupted.

"That doesn't sound reasonable at all. We, the ghost crabs, are responsible for this wonderful sand. We have broken it up using our pincers while we look for invertebrates to feed on."

The creatures started to buzz; both theories seemed improbable and unrealistic. Mr. Flamingo called for order in the assembly, and then Mrs. Green Sea Turtle spoke.

"I believe this beach is different than the western one because of us, the sea turtles. The only reason we come to shore is to nest, and we do it on the same beaches where we hatched. My ancestors chose this place to lay their eggs, therefore I come back every 3 years to do the same. When we are not in Galápagos we are traveling anywhere in the Pacific Ocean. I have been to places as remote as the Marquesas Islands, 3000 miles farther west. My fellow turtles do the same, and cruise all over. So each and every one of us has brought little grains of sand from other regions, building up this beach with fine material from somewhere else."

At that precise moment the sky darkened for a few seconds. A huge black bird approached the group. It was Mr. Frigatebird. He softly landed on the driftwood's dead branch. After politely greeting everyone, he cleared his throat to catch the attention of the audience. When he was ready to speak, Mrs. Sea Turtle interrupted abruptly.

"How dare you be here! You, pirate, thief, you should be ashamed! You eat my dear turtle hatchlings. Right after they dig their way up, 2 or 3 feet through the sand, just when they are willing to walk down to the water, you catch them with no mercy. You don't give them a chance. My poor little turtles, you are a thief, ugly, hateful, evil…"

"Wait a second Madam. I am not a thief! I am a 'kleptoparasite'. There is even a scientific word to describe my behavior. You well know I cannot dive, my feathers are not waterproof, so I have no choice than to steal food. I must survive too, you know!"

"But you survive by doing harm to others…"

"Listen madam, at least I take care of my own chicks. You, turtles of the world, simply lay your eggs, and then leave them! It is not my fault that you are such bad parents…"

Mr. Pink Flamingo couldn't allow the quarrel to go on. For the sake of the meeting, he asked the frigate, in a very courteous manner, to take off and come back another day. The frigate departed with dignity, leaving behind a very upset turtle. And by now no one had had the opportunity to listen to Mr. Frigate's theory.

The creatures were all commenting on the episode, when a soft voice interrupted the loud chat.

"I know the answer."

It was the parrotfish; a creature colored in bizarre combinations of greens and blues highlighted with reds and yellows. Everyone was surprised by the presence of the parrotfish; he hadn't been invited because he was not precisely considered a wise creature. They laughed.

"You know the answer? You spend your life biting off coral! How can a beauty like you have a brain?" asked the turtle.

“Let me tell you that we, the parrotfishes, are responsible for producing this fine sand. Didn’t you say I spend my life eating coral? That’s right, we scrape polyps and algae from hard white coral. We take in the coral and grind it in our gullets to extract the food. Then we excrete the hard stuff in the form of very fine sand,” explained the parrotfish.

“So you are saying that this sand is not more than parrotfish poop. You are overly arrogant!” exclaimed the ray.

“What I am saying is completely true. We can produce from 10 to 50 pounds of sand per year. Do you want me to show you our crushing machinery?” challenged the parrotfish.

Everyone nodded their heads in agreement. They needed proof to believe such an amazing story. At that point the parrotfish opened its “beak” and showed another set of jaws he had deep in his throat, strong and hard, appropriate tools for milling the coral.

“Did you see? Those are my ‘pharyngeal jaws’, extra jaws to turn huge amounts of white coral into powder. In other words, I can shop quickly and do the kitchen work later. Algae or polyps need not be separated from the chunks of coral in which they are embedded. I swallow the whole thing, pass it on to the pharyngeal jaws, crush the hard material and extract the digestible food. I eliminate the rest as white sand.”

This was too much information for all the Wisest creatures’ brains to process at once. They asked for a fifteen-minute break to think about the parrotfish statement. Then, as they were very democratic, they voted to give a verdict. Mr. Pink Flamingo delivered the judgment.

“By the Wisest Creatures decree we believe you. That does explain the formation of the sand. But then why is it that this sand is found only on the eastern beach and not on the western beach of the same point of land?”

"Let me tell you, wise creatures, that this is due to the prevailing winds and currents. Haven't you noticed that the ocean currents come from the southeast for most of the year? So those currents carry the floating stuff I make in the ocean to the eastern beach. The western beach is the sheltered side, hence the erosion of land and not sea material is dominant, and the beach has taken the color of the surrounding rocks which are rich in green and black minerals," answered the parrotfish overconfidently.

Every one of the guests was astonished. Such an apparently insignificant fish had found the right answer. Now everything was clear. The beaches exposed to the prevailing currents were mainly made up of shells and coral, once-living and lightweight material brought up by the sea. The western beaches of the islands were sometimes black, sometimes red or even green. They are largely composed by heavy inorganic grains coming from the rocks and volcanoes closeby.

The parrotfish was a bright fish, not only in coloration, but also of mind. A fish with a smart mind! They unanimously declared him the wisest of all creatures, from the land and from the sea.

The wisest felt proud and relieved. They had finally found the answer to a long-sought mystery. It was time to go back to their places and duties. No one moved however. They stared at each other, motionless around the driftwood. None of them wanted to step on a white beach made up of parrotfish poop.

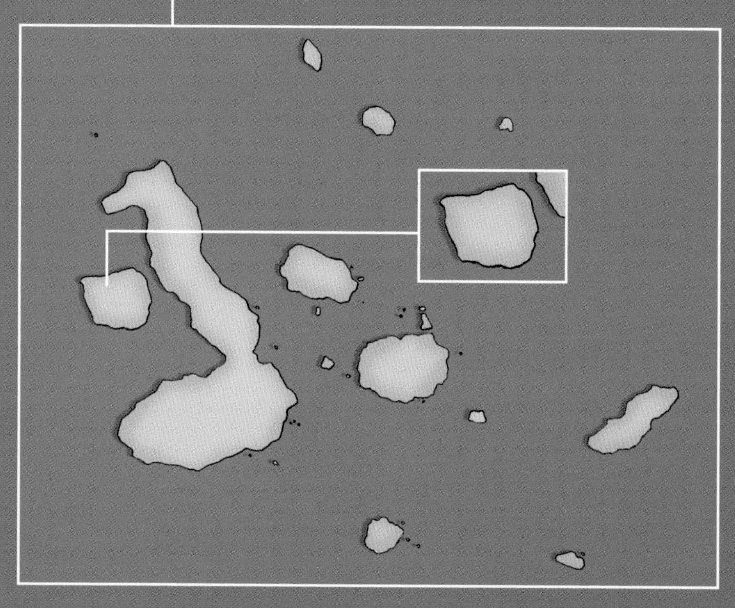

Galápagos cormorants do not fly
maybe because once upon a time...

Fernandina bedtime story

Every day, after diving and fishing, Fernandina Flightless Cormorants come back to the rocks to dry their wing feathers, spreading them out as if being proud of their tiny size. Or maybe they indeed are proud; maybe they do know that they are a great example of evolution, and that they are the only flightless cormorants in the world. Maybe they believe that…

…Once upon a time there was an explorer that arrived by chance to the Galápagos archipelago. It was a web-footed bird, with a long sinuous neck and stiff tail. His eyes were well adapted to see underwater. It was a cormorant, a kind of sea bird that belongs to the order of Pelicans.

The feathered creature was leaving its family behind in the search of new places, areas with less competitors and predators. By fortune he got to Galápagos, isolated islands in the Pacific Ocean, away from everything the cormorant had known until then. And of all the islands, he arrived to Fernandina, the youngest.

At first sight the place was disappointing. It looked desolated and barren; it was made of lava and only lava. In the distance he could hear the earth rumbling, as if heavy stones were dropping somewhere in the higher elevations. The cormorant was afraid to move, and for days he remained hidden in the crop of mangrove trees fearing the worst: the sky falling on his head.

Mangroves were the only familiar things to the cormorant. The exact same mangroves grew along the shorelines of the land he had left behind. He felt close to those plants that had probably arrived from the same place, and, as he was to discover, found it suitable for survival in this desert island. But he was different from mangroves; those plants needed less. He needed food, shelter, and love.

Each night the earth trembled and its clamor was unbearable. Finally the cormorant gained some courage and went to look for the horrible sound's origin.

He flew up, following the gentle slopes of the island, to discover that its whole landmass was actually one huge active volcano. But instead of fear, he experienced a growing curiosity. He was intrigued by the rivers of lava running down from the summit. They resembled melted caramel. He watched the ash and rock showers with awe and enjoyed the reverberation of gas extruded to the atmosphere. The island was beautiful, strange, and yet splendid.

The cormorant desperately wanted to inspect his new home, but his belly begged for food after days of starvation. He flew back to the shoreline and dove in the shallow sea. Chilly water! He'd never felt anything as freezing! Nevertheless he did not need to swim for too long, because the cool water was rich in fish.

Fernandina was a truly peculiar place. The land often trembled, as if the volcano wanted to communicate with the living things on it. There were not many plants or animals. Food was plenty, and there were no big mammals to be afraid of.

Every day the cormorant explored new sites. He loved to watch the odd shapes of lava as well as the immensity of the caldera in the middle of the volcano.

During his first weeks on the island, the cormorant slept in the mangroves, a safe place to avoid predation. Then he simply passed the nights on the warmer lava. Anyway, it turned out that there was no danger in his new home. No dogs, no rats, no pigs, Fernandina was a true heaven.

Still, he felt lonely. The cormorant needed a friend, a mate!

When he was starting to miss his fellow cormorants, he saw another cormorant landing at the top of the mangroves nearby.

What a coincidence! Something that could possibly occur only once every million years, but the new arrival happened to be a female cormorant, and a very pretty one.

It goes without saying that it was love at first sight. Mr. Cormorant and Mrs. Cormorant married in a red mangrove. He offered her a great bouquet of brown algae and she arranged it at the top of a lava flow, the first addition for their nest. Every time Mr. Cormorant came back from the water, he offered Mrs. Cormorant a new present. Sometimes he brought her sea urchin skeletons, sometimes algae, or drifted twigs. The best gift of all was a sea star that looked like a chocolate chip cookie. Mrs. Cormorant loved it!

Mrs. Cormorant knew it wasn't very conventional to nest on the ground. But she also knew how much Mr. Cormorant loved the lava, and anyhow, there was nothing to fear on the ground, so why not? Why should one do what everyone else does?

After a few honeymoon weeks, Mrs. Cormorant laid two eggs, which hatched within several days. Both parents worked hard, taking turns incubating, and from then on, sharing the work of rearing the little ones.

The eldest chick hatched with big, healthy wings, like its parents'. But the youngest looked different than any other cormorant they had ever seen. It was a fat, heavy chick with tiny wings.

Within several months the eldest began to fly, and the father was proud showing him their vast home island-volcano. The youngest tried arduously, though he never managed to take off. He was awfully heavy, with too little wings. Anyhow, they were all happy. Flying or not, food was close and they swam by using their feet. They had no need of their wings to escape from predators, or to get to trees for nesting. So it did not make any difference being flightless or not.

After a while the Cormorant family discovered that a few other cormorants had also arrived to Fernandina. They were glad to share the island with more of their kind, yet the 2 young cormorants were the happiest because they immediately fell in love with the two new lady cormorants. The cormorant population began to increase.

When the flightless, heavy cormorant had chicks, the entire bird community came to the nest to see if they hatched with either big or small wings. They both inherited little wings, just like the father's. They were named Aptero and Aptera.

By that time there were a few other young cormorants on the island. They laughed at the size of Aptero and Aptera's wings. When everyone flew away to explore the island, Aptero and Aptera waited on the shore, lonely and sad. They did not like to be different, overly different.

However, the flightless siblings were the diving champions. They were much heavier, so they could go deeper, and stay longer underwater. They used their rather large tails for steering, catching the largest and most juicy octopi and eels. Year after year they won the prizes as the best divers of Fernandina Cormorants. Aptero and Aptera were both flightless birds, and even though their wings looked slightly ridiculous, they finally gained the respect of the other cormorants.

One year the waters heated up, the temperature of the ocean got many degrees hotter than it ever had before. Warm waters are poor in nutrients; so fish move deeper in the ocean, where the sea is still cool, and they can find more food. This event is known as "El Niño". Every several years, for a reason not well understood, the waters of the Eastern Pacific warm up, turning the whole planet's climate upside down.

The cormorants needed to dive deeper and deeper to nourish themselves. Every day proved more difficult to catch fish for their hungry chicks. The only ones that faced no problems finding food were the heavy great divers, Aptero and Aptera. They always brought something to their respective families, living on the lava flows of Fernandina Island.

The flying cormorants became fewer and fewer, and one day they were all gone. The single ones left on the island were Aptero, Aptera and their descendants. They had been the best suited to survive, so within several generations, the island was populated by this new kind of bird: the flightless cormorant. They had afforded being flightless because of the lack of predators. With the reduction of their flight muscles, there was a great saving of energy that could be invested in larger legs. They became the biggest cormorants in the world, diving to depths of more than 100 feet. They never learned about fear.

Today, flightless cormorants populate the coolest parts of Galápagos, living on Fernandina and the western coast of Isabela, where the sea life is richest.

Every day, after diving and fishing, Fernandina Flightless Cormorants come back to the rocks to dry their wing feathers, spreading them out as if being proud of their tiny size. Or maybe they indeed are proud; maybe they do know that they are a great example of evolution, and that they are the only flightless cormorants in the world. Maybe they believe that…

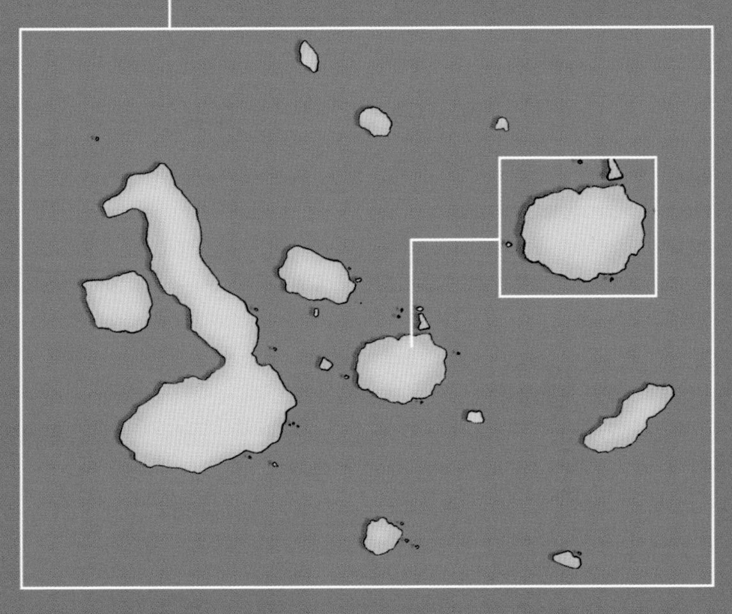

The Galápagos cowboy kid who cared for his home islands

Santa Cruz bedtime story

Diego was a handsome boy, a kid of big round eyes and tanned skin who lived on the second largest island in the Galápagos, Santa Cruz.

He inhabited the southern highlands of the island, 1500 feet above sea level. That area of Santa Cruz got a lot of moisture that, combined with the fertile soil, made the place rich in lush vegetation. It was ideal ground for growing tropical plants and raising cattle, so Ecuadorians had settled there since the 1940's.

Diego's parents had a cattle farm. With the milk they made cheese, butter and wonderful desserts. Like all kids in the highlands, Diego had a few chores after school. But for the boy, his duties were sweet every day pastimes. Diego was in charge of herding the cattle in the afternoons. He also had to milk the cows twice a week. He was a true Galápagos cowboy kid! He loved riding his horse to take the animals out to pasture. Seated in the saddle he could see blue ocean all around, and view the far off islands he hadn't visited yet.

Diego's school was several miles away from his home. Together with his 2 brothers, they rode on the same horse to class, where they met with friends from the other highland farms.

Very often during the "Garua" season, the kids got wet in the mist on their way to school. So their day frequently had to begin with the teacher letting them dry first, while telling stories about the people who had come to the Galápagos in the early years, and about the fearless animals that populated the archipelago. Diego loved the mist; he loved to hear the stories.

His was a very small school, with just a few students. They had one teacher for all the different grades, and they shared the same room. Furniture was made of wood, from the Spanish cedars that grew in the area. Every day during break, they played soccer. They couldn't live without soccer.

One of Diego's past-times after school was to visit the pond at the outer edge of his farm. He and his brothers would sit down for long hours watching the different birds flying in either to drink water, or to preen their feathers. Darwin's finches were fascinating. They were not bright, but they featured all kinds of beak shapes and sizes. White-cheeked pintail ducks often swam in the pond. The most colorful bird of the area, the vermilion flycatcher, took long baths in the murky water. But Diego's favorite animal was the giant tortoise, and particularly one tortoise he named José.

José was a large male tortoise. Diego knew it because males were the biggest, sporting long tails. José's carapace was shaped like a dome. The teacher had told them that tortoises inhabiting the largest islands, with lots of low vegetation, were dome-shaped, as the food was easily accessible and their heads didn't have to go very high to reach it. But tortoises from arid little islands were smaller, with a shell shaped like a saddle. That shape was due to the long necks they had, necessary for reaching the cactus pads hanging high above the ground. There were 11 different kinds of tortoises in the Galápagos, and Santa Cruz Island held one of the largest and healthiest races.

Diego recognized his tortoise friend due to a scar on the left side of the shell. "How did he get it?" wondered the boy.

On weekends Diego's family would take a bus ride to the largest town in Galápagos, Puerto Ayora, which was on the coast. There they would shop and enjoy the sea.

In those years, the late 1970's, the village had only a few thousand inhabitants, but for Diego that was already like a metropolis. He felt shy meeting so many people. Nevertheless, the joy of swimming in the turquoise water blew away his fears. The kids mingled at the main dock to play different games. They jumped off the jetty, performing all sorts of acrobatics. Their favorite game was "hide and seek", but played in the water.

In the meantime Diego's parents exchanged cheese and beef for fish and seafood. They hardly ever used any money. What for? They lived in heaven!

Once a month a cargo ship would arrive to the island bringing all kinds of supplies. Not long ago it had brought the first ice cream, and the boy just fell in love with it. The ship would return to the mainland with some cattle from the family's farm. Sometimes his father would go too.

When his father came back from Ecuador, he would bring great toys for his children. They would always get a new soccer ball and stories, many stories about life across the 600 nautical miles of ocean.

The family would gather in the evenings to share anecdotes, or to talk about the old days when there wasn't a road to town and the grandparents would ride by donkey for a few days to get there.

Diego did not own a television. Nobody on the island owned one. They did not need a TV, living in such a wonderful place. They could ride horses, run through the elephant-grass fields, climb fruit trees, and above all they could talk, enjoying each other's company. Diego could also count on the friendship of his favorite tortoise.

The boy was growing up as a cheerful child, a master of his own world.

One weekend in Puerto Ayora, he had an experience that would influence him very deeply. It was an experience that would make him a determined protector of Galápagos.

He was walking to a beautiful beach called Tortuga bay. It was a two-hour hike through the arid vegetation of Santa Cruz Island. Behind a giant prickly pear cactus he saw a pile of odd-looking rocks, too rounded compared to the rough, uneven lava of the trail. Upon closer inspection, he discovered that it was not a collection of rocks at all, but a group of small tortoises. Babies! But there was something wrong with them; they were too still, quiet and breathless. After a few minutes, Diego discovered something horrible: the tortoises were all dead! They had been killed. The carapaces showed big holes, and they were empty inside: the insides of the tortoises had been taken out. Diego was completely shocked. He remained immobile for a long while, unable to believe his eyes. Suddenly a rat rushed away from the dreadful pile. It had been the rats! They had committed this terrible murder!

Diego reacted at last, and the only thing he could do was run. He wanted to go to town to warn people, to urge them to stop the rats. There could be more baby tortoises in danger!

Running as fast as he could, Diego bumped into a tall man that happened to be walking on the road. The boy could hardly speak as he told his story. The fellow did not show much sympathy for the kid, but asked Diego to take him to the terrible place. When they got there, the man inspected the empty carapaces and agreed: it had been the rats, the Norwegian rats that had been introduced long ago, probably on the ships of pirates and whalers.

Diego was expecting the man to do something about it but he did not know what exactly. He was hoping for a scientific explanation, for a remedy to the terrible event. However, instead of granting some relief to Diego, the man reproached, "if we did not have people living in Galápagos this sort of thing wouldn't happen. This would be a true heaven. It is the settlers that have destroyed the islands! There is nothing else to do now, just to take some of these dead tortoises to my lab for research." He collected a few shells and walked away, without more words. The boy remained behind, speechless and disturbed.

The terrible sentences reverberated in Diego's mind. The man had meant that it was because of them, the inhabitants of Galápagos, that the islands and their animals were suffering. So if there weren't people around, the archipelago would be perfect and pristine. Diego felt really guilty, broken hearted! His family had been living in Santa Cruz Island for three generations. They had never killed a Galápagos animal. Why was it wrong to live there? He did not know of any friends or family who were capable of bringing rats. Was it true that the islands were threatened because of them…because of him? Diego felt terribly sad. He did not want his home islands, and his favorite animals, the tortoises, to disappear. Maybe it had been a rat that made the scar on José's shell when José was a young tortoise!

The boy cried and couldn't stop crying. He wandered around aimlessly for an undetermined time, until he eventually ran into thick dust. Diego looked up and discovered that there was a Park ranger digging in the ground and producing all that dust. The ranger greeted the boy, and immediately noticed that he had been crying. Instead of inquiring the reason for those tears, the Park ranger asked the kid to give him a hand. He was convinced that keeping children busy was the best way to cheer them up.

So the boy stayed to help the ranger. He did not know why, but like a robot, he started scooping without saying a word. His mind was too distressed to think about the reason for being there, in the middle of the arid zone, excavating a hole. They hadn't gone deep when Diego discovered what they were digging for. He couldn't believe what he saw! Tears sprouted again. There were 10 white tortoise eggs! What were they doing? He looked at the ranger with fury and anger, and wanted to bite the man. But before Diego could move the ranger explained, "relax boy, we are doing this to help those tortoise eggs. We will carefully put them in a box, take them to the Charles Darwin Station- National Park Service, and incubate them for three or four months. When the babies hatch, we'll take care of them for the next five years, and only then will we send them back."

"But if you send them back, the rats will eat them!"

"When they are five, they are big enough, and their carapace is hard enough, so they do not have any predators at all."

"So these eggs are going to make it. Do you promise me that?"
"Yes, but they will make it with your help. Let's put them in the box. Anytime you can, pass by the National Park Service and give me a hand with them."

"I don't know if I will be able to do so. I must leave Galápagos. People are bad to the islands. I should leave."

"If you leave, if everyone leaves, who is going to help the tortoises then? Who will collect the eggs, and who will take care of the babies? Who will be here to get rid of the rats and help with the other problems?"
"I don't know. I am so confused now."

"Humans can be destructive, but people with education and love can be helpful to Galápagos. Talk to your father about it."

The boy finally felt some relief, but he still had remorse and doubts.

It was late and his family was going to worry if he didn't get back in time. He said farewell to the ranger and went back to the road to hitch a ride to the highlands. He wanted to see José, his tortoise friend, before talking to his father, so he went to the pond first.

When he got to the pond he was surprised to meet his whole family: dad, mom and his brothers.

"Where have you been? We need one more hand here! José is upside down and we can not leave him like that. Come and help!" said the father.

The boy used all his strength, and in a moment, with everyone's help, José was upright. Diego felt so happy this time. He was actually doing something good for his islands, and for his friend José the tortoise!

The kids applauded to celebrate their success but Diego clapped the most. He felt good. However, he needed to share his distrust with the family. He told them about the dead tortoises, about the tall man, and about the Park ranger.

"Dear Diego," said his father, "have no more doubts. You have now experienced how good people can be for these islands. Besides, you are not guilty of anything, neither are we. Rats, goats and pigs were introduced long ago, even before settlers came to Galápagos. Whalers brought most of them, some by accident and some on purpose. If we all leave, who is going to take care of these islands? Who will assist with the raising and breeding programs of the tortoises? And who will tell the world about the beauty of Galápagos? It is true that human beings can be very destructive, but we can also learn from our mistakes. Galápagos could be a great experiment, and you could be part of it. We will prove that there are people who care about the environment, that human beings and nature can live together."

"Do you really believe we mean no harm to the creatures of Galápagos?" asked Diego.

"Some people haven't yet learned about the importance of this place. They only arrived here in the last few years. But our duty is to teach them about Galápagos. Then they will love the islands as you do, and they will help us to protect them. Wipe away those tears, because you have already helped your animal friends, your tortoise friend José. And you can keep doing the good work. Go back to the National Park Service and Charles Darwin Station, and help them whenever you have the time," said his father.

Diego cheered up. His father was right, he could do good things for the Galápagos. He grabbed his father's hand and walked home with the rest of the family.

The next morning the boy woke up very early. He dressed in his school uniform, and, together with his brothers, rode the horse to school.

That day was going to be a grand day. Diego was going to tell his classmates about the rats, the tortoises, but also about the great experiment of which they were all a part. He would teach his friends that they were capable of showing to the world that with love and education it could be possible to live in balance, human beings and nature. He would take his classmates to the National Park Service to help with the program to raise Galápagos Tortoises. They would become the young Park rangers of the Galápagos Islands.

Diego, the young Galápagos cowboy, was definitely determined to protect his islands, which were his home, and the home of José-tortoise.

One day in the life of a swallow-tailed gull

Genovesa bedtime story

My name is Blanca, and I live in one of the nicest places imaginable. My home is an island known as the “Bird Island”. It is Tower, or Genovesa, located on the northeastern corner of the Galápagos archipelago.

This is a small island, but it is a haven for birds. There are more than one million feathered creatures, crowding the trees, the bushes, and the lava fields.

Genovesa is an extinct volcano. Its summit collapsed forming one gigantic crater, known as a caldera. The ocean eroded part of the caldera's rim, so it became a beautiful bay, Darwin Bay.

My day actually begins at dusk, when I leave the island to search for food, because I fish at night! I am very proud of being the only gull in the whole world that fishes at night. I can fly miles away, and sometimes I am gone for days in a row. My favorite food is squid. I just love squid. It is juicy, it is chewy, and it shines in the dark.

Sometimes I follow boats, because as they move through the water they make the squid and other tiny organisms light up. I see the sparkles and I dip my head in the water to catch my meal. The light they produce is called bioluminescence, as it is light created by living creatures. When people see me in the dark through their boat windows they get frightened at first because they think I am a ghost. I look so extremely white when I am fishing at night that some call me the "ghost" of Galápagos.

After eating my meal, I come back to my beautiful island from about midnight onwards. There is a lot of activity early in the morning. The swallow-tailed gull chicks are waiting for their parents. One can see a lot of "throwing up" or, in other words, "regurgitation".

Parents bring up the squid they have eaten that night for chicks to swallow. If the squid is larger than the baby, the parents must re-swallow, digest a bit more and regurgitate it several times. Both mother and father take care of the little ones, and pairs remain together for their entire lives. We don't breed in any specific season so it's possible to find swallow-tailed gull chicks year-round.

I have many friends in my home island. They are active at daytime, while I try to rest. I like the three kinds of booby very much. I am amazed by their diving skills. They plunge into the ocean completely and go down several feet to catch fish. They all use the same technique, but to avoid competition they obtain their food from different places. The red-footed boobies go farther from shore, the Nazca boobies stay in-between the islands and the blue-footed boobies fish really close to shore. In that way they find enough for everyone. I admire their organization.

The red-footed boobies have feet as pretty as mine: red. I love their beaks: blue with a hint of pink. The Nazca boobies do not have a particularly amazing foot color, however, they can sometimes be really interesting creatures. I once saw a Nazca booby incubating a couple of rocks for several weeks: he thought they were his eggs! But the most unbelievable thing I saw was a Nazca booby who adopted a frigate chick for months. It could not feed it, but nevertheless was always there for the chick. What an excellent babysitter! The visitors and scientists were also surprised to see that happen.

Blue-footed boobies are not common in my home island, but whenever I have the chance to see them dance, I do. They are wonderfully coordinated. The male raises one foot, the female does it too, they give little presents to each other and finally they open their wings and point to the sky with tail and beak. I love their dances!

My island is a gigantic nesting colony of frigate birds. I like to call it a "frigaterie". All day long I hear gulls and boobies screaming when frigates approach. Frigates can be a problem now and then. They chase us to make us throw up our meals, and sometimes they rob our chicks. But most of the times they just go out to sea. They have great long beaks, so they "hook up" the fish they find on the surface of the ocean.

In April and May the shores of my island change in color. They become almost completely red because of the many male frigates that hang out together to impress the flying females. They inflate huge red balloons or sacs found under their bills. I guess the females go for the largest or the brightest. I wouldn't particularly like such a show-off male, yet fortunately I am a gull, and not a freaky frigate.

There are a handful of land birds on Genovesa. The curious Galápagos mockingbirds and the good-looking Galápagos dove. There are also some finches, four kinds to be precise. The most remarkable is the "vampire" finch. It has a reputation of drinking blood from boobies, but they only do it during extremely dry seasons.

We are very lucky on my bird island, because it lacks Galápagos hawks. Yes! They don't live here. They can not live in a place where there are no lava lizards. Who could imagine such a thing? However it seems that even though hawks are at the top of the food chain and able to eat us all, they need to count on the always-available prey, the lava lizard.

Speaking of lizards, I must say that there are no land reptiles on my island. It is the one true "Bird Island". The only reptiles we sometimes see are the tiny and very black marine iguanas.

When I think about the creatures that share this island with me, I am amazed by the many connections one can find. The water is warmer, so there is more coral. There are no land reptiles, so the cacti possess soft spines, as they don't need protection from tortoises or land iguanas. There are no lizards, therefore there are no hawks. Owls, which are supposed to hunt at night, in my island hunt in the daytime.

In the afternoon I often take a bath in the middle of the caldera. I can hear the noise of red-billed tropicbirds coming back from the cliffs. They are so graceful, with a red beak and long white tails. I like birds that show red somewhere on them. I am not jealous of their beauty because we, the swallow-tailed gulls, are smarter. Tropicbirds fish during the day, so they have more competition than we do. And they have more encounters with the "pirate" frigates than we do, because we fish at night.

Late in the afternoon I get ready to go to sea again. I can never manage a good sleep because of the noise from boobies, frigates, tropicbirds, and the rest of the inhabitants of my island. But I don't complain since sharing my day with them is a lot of fun.

I am proud of Genovesa, and I am very proud of being a swallow-tailed gull, the only gull in the world that goes fishing at night.

Rumina, the sea lion that counted Bartolomé volcanoes every morning

Bartolomé bedtime story

This is the story of Rumina, a Galápagos sea lion, who counted her island volcanoes every morning. She lived in Bartolomé, a little island in the middle of the Galápagos, made of rocks of unique colors and textures.

Countless small, brown peaks known as spatter cones cover the highest elevations of Bartolomé. The oldest part of the island is made of volcanic ash, created through explosive eruptions of lava cooling off with water. The compacted ash is called tuff. However tuff, is not tough at all. With the action of the waves and wind, tuff has been transformed into yellow-brown sand that makes up two great beaches, one on each side of the island. Next to the northern beach there is still a piece of the ash volcano, an impressive rock known as “Pinnacle Rock”.

Around Pinnacle Rock there was a small colony of sea lions. They would spend a lot of time sunbathing on the layers of flat ash, but the young ones also loved to swim and get in the water to practice several kinds of games.

When their mothers went out to fish, the sea lion pups grouped in gangs to play. They spent hours and hours enjoying themselves.

Rumina was one of them. She was a very athletic pup, the fastest and the best surfer of the group. No other young sea lion could catch her when they played “hide and seek”. She knew how to take the waves at their break point and ride the pipeline.

Rumina liked to invent games. She discovered that during low tide, most of the marine iguanas headed to the water to feed on algae. So at that time, every day, she called her friends to pull iguana tails. The sea lion that had pulled the most won the game.

Rumina found out that penguins ate little anchovies and sardines. She saw them working as a team to trap the fish in a big bubble. Whenever she encountered a thick school of small fish, she looked for penguins. She tried to be as fast as them, but penguins could swim up to 20 mph. Anyhow, Rumina tried. She knew that penguins are birds, so they hatch from eggs, and that sea lions are mammals, born directly from their mothers. However, they shared two things: penguins flew through the water flapping their wings, just like sea lions used their front flippers to swim. Galápagos penguins and Galápagos sea lions were both able to live on the equator thanks to the cool currents that bathed the islands. Cool water meant an abundance of fish.

Of all her pastimes, Rumina's passion was geology. As soon as she opened her eyes every morning, she counted Bartolomé's little spatter cones, to see if a new one had been formed overnight, but she always ended up with the same number. Bartolomé was not an active island anymore. It was in the middle of Galápagos, and volcanism occurred only in the west. Rumina didn't know that however, so she longed for an eruption. She needed a lot of imagination to understand how Bartolomé's volcanoes originated. Geology would be much clearer if she could watch volcanoes in action.

Rumina and her playmates began to explore the farther shores. They swam to the black lava flow in front of Bartolomé, called Sullivan Bay, on Santiago Island.

Sullivan Bay looked barren because it was pretty young, only formed in the late 1800's. Rumina wondered about the odd shapes in the lava. Most of it resembled many ropes put together; she would later learn its name, "pahoe-hoe". It was such a fun word that she said it over and over again for a whole day! 'Pah-hoy-hoy! Pah-hoy-hoy! Pah-hoy-hoy-hoy-who!' It just about drove her poor mother crazy, but she was proud that Rumina had learned so much.

Diving along the shoreline of Sullivan Bay, Rumina discovered lava tunnels. Sullivan's geology was definitely fascinating, so the young sea lion convinced her friends to go there every day.

The mother sea lions did not want their pups playing too far from Bartolomé's nursery. Therefore, late in the afternoon, all the youngsters hurried back to meet their moms before they found out what was going on.

On one of those days, as they were crossing the channel between Sullivan and Bartolomé, Rumina saw a gigantic fin heading slowly towards them. The fin moved from side to side. It was the fin of a shark!

Rumina's heart stopped. That is why the mothers did not want the pups playing away from the nursery: big sharks could eat them! What was she going to do now? Her friends were in danger and it was her fault.

She alerted her playmates to swim quickly to Bartolomé's shores. The sea lions jumped in a "porpoise-like" way, in order to move faster, and managed to escape. But Rumina had lost vital seconds while warning the others. It was too late for her!

Nevertheless, when the creature, indeed a shark, got closer, it greeted her in a gentle manner. What a relief! It happened to be the least harmful of sea monsters, a whale shark. It was as big as a whale, but was actually a fish, the largest on the planet. And they don't eat sea lions; they only eat plankton, which are the tiny animals and plants of the ocean.

Rumina, still astonished, barely managed to say hello. The very polite whale shark excused himself for cruising through those waters. He had been so busy eating little shrimp that he had lost his course. Now he was going to head west, toward the erupting island, Fernandina.

Rumina's eyes shone, her whiskers stood up. The shark was actually going to an active island! Fernandina was erupting right then! But why Fernandina and not her own island, Bartolomé?

The whale shark was a wise, old creature who knew it all. He kindly explained to her the reason why western islands, like Fernandina, are active and young; while central islands, like Bartolomé, are not active anymore. This was because the Galápagos archipelago moves as a whole. It is on a plate, a piece of the earth crust. That plate, he illustrated, was like thick foam floating on the surface of the ocean. It was shifting to the southeast, sinking beneath the coast of South America. The heat for the eruptions was provided by the so-called "hot spot" located underneath the Western Islands. A hotspot is motionless and is deep within the earth. So after a volcano is formed, it is carried away on the constantly moving plate, and then a new volcano appears and so on and so on.

It was clear for Rumina now that those islands far from the hot spot shouldn't be active anymore, so she couldn't expect an eruption in Bartolomé, her home. She had to go west.

Rumina wanted to ask the shark to take her on his trip to Fernandina, but she knew that she was too young to leave home. She depended completely on her mother's milk and care. She had no choice but to let the whale shark go, just hoping that the eruption lasted until she grew up.

Rumina went back to the nursery to meet her mother. She always recognized her sweet mother's call as her mother recognized Rumina's answer. It was wonderful when they found each other. They played for a while in the water, making mellow noises, and smelling one another. Then they looked for a comfortable rock, and Mom nursed her lovely pup.

Rumina was growing up very healthy. She regularly surfed, and explored her surroundings, and every morning, as a mandatory duty, she counted the spatter cones of Bartolomé. She cherished the hope of one day discovering a new little volcano.

When she was almost a year old, her mother invited her to come on a fishing voyage. She needed to learn to catch fish. Mom felt proud of her daughter, she was one of the quickest sea lions she had ever met. Soon Rumina wouldn't need mother's milk and protection.

They adventured farther and farther out to sea. One day, Rumina asked her mom if they could explore the westernmost island, Fernandina. Rumina gave good reasons. There were upwellings of a cool current, called the Cromwell current. This was rich in nutrients and therefore rich in fish. Fernandina was also the youngest island in Galápagos and Rumina longed for it to still be erupting, as the whale shark had told her months before. They could go, spend some time there, and soon afterward come back to Bartolomé.

Rumina's mother tenderly looked at her beautiful daughter. She had matured as a strong adult sea lion, ready to go out on her own. It was time for Rumina to become independent, so the mother encouraged her to fulfill her dream and adventure alone.

The young sea lion felt a bit overwhelmed by the responsibility of being a grown-up. But the desire of traveling to Fernandina was irresistible. Therefore she decided to go and see the eruption.

Rumina departed bearing west. She swam along the northern coast of Santiago Island. At night she looked for good ledges of lava where she could sleep and rest. In a few days, she was crossing to Isabela, the largest island. She followed the northern shores. Isabela revealed wonderful volcanoes; it was actually made of 6 big ones with shield shapes. Rumina met the Galápagos fur seals on Isabela. They were her relatives, within her same family, but smaller in size with bear-like heads and a lot of fur.

She wondered why people called them seals, when they were not seals at all. They possessed external ears and swam using their front flippers, as sea lions do. True seals do not have ear-flaps and propel themselves with their hind flippers. The fur seals greeted her with kindness and showed her the way to Fernandina Island.

Rumina feared that the eruption had stopped by then. Nonetheless, volcanoes can be active for months, and sometimes even for years. Within a few hours she crossed to the young and pristine Fernandina Island and easily came upon the eruption. The fumes in the air and the increasing heat guided the young sea lion to the right place.

When she finally saw the eruption, she understood it all. The reddish yellow lava was very hot, so it moved fast. The surface cooled most rapidly because of its contact with air. Therefore a smooth, ropy exterior formed at the crust. Now she could comprehend the pahoe-hoe lava on Sullivan Bay.

She saw molten rock flowing down, the outsides were solid, but the insides continued to move. Eventually, when the source of lava stopped, there was not enough of it to fill the whole flow, and an empty space formed: a lava tunnel!

Close to the vent from where the lava emerged, she witnessed dramatic fire fountains. As large amounts of gas were released, large lumps of molten rock were sent skyward. These landed and cooled to look like cowpatties, which piled up on each other. That was how spatter cones formed! Now she knew the story behind her beloved tiny Bartolomé cones, the ones she used to count every morning.

Rumina was looking at the present to understand the past; looking at Fernandina's eruption to understand the way her own island had originated.

It was clear now! Rumina had become a true geologist. She had explored and learned. She felt ready to go back home and keep up with research, but in her own island. Rumina swam back home.

On the ash layers around the pinnacle rock of Bartolomé Island, Rumina, the geologist sea lion, while resting in the late afternoons, would tell the others the way the Galápagos Islands formed. She could explain many features, like tunnels and pahoe-hoe lavas, ash, cinder and spatter cones. She would tell every creature that they shouldn't expect an eruption in the central part of Galápagos, because of the plate moving southeast and the hotspot on the west.

However, she kept her usual habit. The first thing she did in the morning, right after opening one eye, was to count each and every one of Bartolomé Island's spatter cones.

Perhaps a new volcano had formed overnight. One never knows!

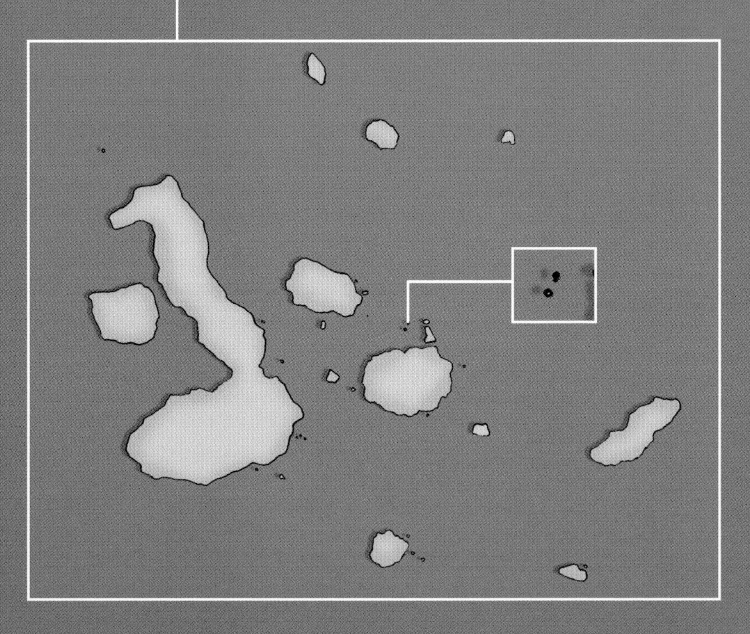

Stefan little beak, the finch who wanted to meet Darwin

Daphne Major bedtime story

Stefan Little Beak was a very curious Darwin finch. He inhabited an island with a crater; actually, the whole island was mainly a crater. It was Daphne Major, an ash cone in the middle of the sea, located in the very heart of Galápagos.

Daphne was a wonderful place to live. However, after a while, it became too small for such a curious and adventurous finch. Stefan wanted to visit the bigger islands, the ones he could see from Daphne. He wanted to go even further away, to learn about the world and its laws. He was so thirsty for knowledge that no one could stop him asking about the nature of things.

His parents couldn't find any more answers for Stefan Little Beak's questions. His father taught him to sing, as every male does. Singing was important in the finch courtship. But he couldn't handle his son's infinite curiosity.

"What makes a finch a finch, and not a mockingbird, or a warbler, or a frigatebird?"

"Are all the finches the same?"

Stefan's parents decided to ask for help from the oldest cactus finch of the island. She was a wise finch.

"Listen, Stefan Little Beak, finches are different from mockingbirds, and from warblers because we are different sorts of creatures, different species you know. Even among the Darwin finches we are 13 kinds, all distinct from each other," spoke the wise cactus finch.

"What is a species?" asked Stefan.

"A species is a group of organisms that resemble one another closely, a group that can only breed with their own kind, and not with others. Like the medium-beak ground Darwin finches of this island, they can only breed with medium-beak ground finches to produce offspring. Mockingbirds can only breed with mockingbirds."

"But my aunt Suzy Medium-Beak married a cactus finch, and they had chicks. How come?" inquired Stefan.

“Sometimes those things happen. Like the horse and the donkey, they are different species and yet occasionally they interbreed. But then the descendant is a ‘hybrid’, and usually hybrids are not able to produce offspring,” the wise cactus finch answered patiently.

“We are all called Darwin finches! So who is Darwin? I want to meet this Darwin. Do you know where to find him?” asked Stefan.

“I am sorry to tell you, my dear, but I don’t know any Darwin. But ask the Galápagos dove, she may know,” replied the wise cactus finch, feeling deeply exhausted.

Stefan flew around to find the dove with red feet and blue eye-rings.

“Do you know who Darwin is and where to find him?” asked Stefan to the dove.

“Darwin is a man with a very long and white beard. I try to stay away from him because my friends told me he likes eating doves. You can find him inside the crater.”

Stefan went inside the crater and indeed discovered a person with a long white beard. Little-Beak was about to land on the man’s shoulder, when he realized that he had a finch in his hand, and that he was doing something with it. So the bird, who was curious but not crazy, decided to wait behind a leaf and watch.

The fellow was measuring the beak of the finch. Then he weighed the creature, put a ring on its leg, and finally released it.

“Well, that didn’t look too painful,” thought Stefan and immediately flew after his colleague to ask him about the man and what he was doing.

"Hi comrade finch, I am Stefan, and I would like to know what that person was doing to you, and if he is Darwin," asked Stefan to the recently tagged and released finch.

"Hello, I am number 72. I am a very important finch because I have a number, and the scientists care about me, my characteristics, and behavior. I am a finch who will make history on this island," responded number 72.

"Was that man Darwin?" asked Stefan.

"You are a funny little-beak. That wasn't Darwin. He is the famous Peter Grant, studying finches together with his wife and fellow researcher, Rosemary, for more than 30 years."

"And why is he so interested in us?" questioned Stefan.

"Because we, the Darwin finches, are a striking example of evolution. A few million years ago our ancestors came to Galápagos. They were different from us. After all this time they evolved into, not only one or two, but 13 different species! As Peter says to me so often, from one ancestor we 'radiated' into 13 kinds. That's why we are so important. And I, number 72, am the most important of all."

"But why was he measuring your beak?" said Stefan.

"Peter and Rosemary want to know about beaks, because the beaks are our tools. You own a little beak, I have a large beak. If there is a drought, and only big, hard seeds that are difficult to open are left on the island, who do you think will survive?" asked number 72, opening his eyes as wide as he could.

“You will,” answered the carefree Stefan. “But now tell me, if it rains a lot, and many small seeds abound, who will be faster in eating them all? Then who will survive?” ingeniously responded Stefan.

“You are a tiny villain! You know nothing and then you come and play the wise finch with me. Go away, I have a lot of scientific work to do.”

So Stefan left number 72. He didn’t like that snobby finch. However, he had learned something new, and he was happy for that. But he still wanted to find the famous Darwin.

He decided to enjoy some fun in the meantime, so he flew around imitating the red-billed tropicbirds in their flight. He must have looked pretty funny. Tropicbirds are many times larger than finches, and they possess long tails when finches look as if someone had cut their tails off.

Anyway, he climbed higher and higher into the air. When he felt he'd reached the top of the world, a real red-billed tropicbird passed by, circled him and asked,

"Are you the finch looking for Darwin?"

"Yes, I am. Do you know where I can find him?"

"I know someone who met Darwin. She lives on Santiago Island, northwest from here," promptly answered the tropicbird.

"I believe that is too far for me. Finches are not long-distance fliers."

"Don't worry, I'll give you a ride," answered the tropicbird kindly.

The friendly red-billed tropicbird put Stefan on his back and headed northwest. It was wonderful to see the ocean so far below. Daphne looked like a twisted cup, containing, instead of coffee or tea, a lot of bubbling life made up of boobies, frigates, and finches.

The flight was rather bumpy because tropicbirds never stop flapping their wings; they also make a loud noise, similar to a referee call. Stefan fully enjoyed the new experience.

After crossing several miles of sea, they arrived to Santiago Island, which was much bigger than Little-Beak's home. A million times bigger!

Santiago had different strips of colors, not like Daphne that was entirely painted in a yellowish-brown hue of volcanic ash. Santiago looked dark green along the shoreline, composed of mangroves. There was the wide whitish-brown section of plants with no leaves: the arid zone. At the top of it all was the light-green humid area. That's where they landed. The tropicbird said farewell and left Stefan in front of a gigantic Galápagos tortoise.

"So you are the finch looking for Darwin?" asked the tortoise.

"Can you help me, madam?"

"I can help you. I have known many of the ones who came through these islands. I met the pirates, I met the whalers, I met Darwin and today, I greet the park rangers that are helping us to get rid of the goats," pronounced the tortoise.

"Tell me about Darwin please," urged Stefan.

"Darwin was a young fellow from a distant country called England," started the tortoise.

"But I heard he had a long white beard," interrupted the finch.

"That's when he grew old. Yet when he came to Galápagos he was only 26 years old. That was in 1835."

"What was he doing here?"

"He was traveling on a ship, the Beagle, mapping this part of the world. Darwin hated to be on the boat. He felt seasick for most of the voyage. So he spent as much time as he could on shore. He spent 19 days on land in the Galápagos, and 9 of those were on this island! That is how I met him," said the tortoise.

"That's not very much time in which to become famous. Why is he so important?" questioned Stefan.

"He collected samples, he did many observations, but not only in Galápagos. His voyage lasted 5 years, and he saw many things. Moreover, he became famous because he thought up his theory of evolution."

"Explain to me please what that means," begged Little-Beak.

"Until Darwin's time, people thought that species did not change. It was commonly believed that the earth had been created the same way as we see it, with its creatures just as they are today. Darwin proposed that the species did change with time, that they do evolve, and he called the mechanism for evolution 'natural selection'."

"But what exactly is 'natural selection'?" said Stefan.

“Do you know what ‘selection’ means?” asked the tortoise.

“Let me think… when I look for seeds, I select the smallest. Yeah! To select is to choose,” answered the finch.

“That’s right, selection is like choosing. However, in nature no one is choosing, it is just that some species make it and some don’t. Like in a race. Those that arrive first win, the others lose. In nature, the winners are those with the best characteristics to make it, and to ‘make it’ means to survive and reproduce. We could say that nature has ‘selected’ them to survive. They will produce offspring and so on.”

“What happens to those that loose the race?” asked Stefan.

“Well, they just don’t make it! They disappear together with those that share their same characteristics. Nevertheless you must remember that nature is always changing. Some are wet years, some become dry years. Some islands hold more vegetation and some are arid. It is a changing environment,” said the tortoise.

“So species are always changing too! Some characteristics can be good for one place, but bad for a different one, or good in one season and bad in another season. It is like the finch beaks on Daphne Major. Number 72 was telling me about the droughts. If there is a drought, the best-suited finches to survive are those with larger beaks. They can eat the only seeds left on the island, those that happen to be the biggest. So after a while only large beaks remain on the island,” Stefan rationalized.

“Exactly! This is called ‘Natural Selection’. It is easy for you to understand. But imagine, in the late 1800’s, it was hard to believe. So some people hated Darwin. However, today we know that he was right, and scientists are finding examples of natural selection everywhere.”

"Yes, I know some scientists on Daphne. They measure finch beaks, and record every change on the island" said Stefan. "But why did they choose Daphne? Santiago is larger, with much more to see. Why are the Grants on Daphne?" wondered the finch.

"You just said it, they want a small island because the changes are much easier to observe and understand in a little area. It is a laboratory of evolution. You shouldn't despise a place just because of its size. After all, Daphne is your home," gently added the tortoise.

"I guess you are right. Daphne is a great place for research, and if I want to take part in the new discoveries, I'd better go back."

"Those are wise words," said the tortoise.

"I will miss your wisdom though," remarked the finch.

"But I believe you are ready to discover things on your own. Anyway you are always welcome to pay me a visit. The tropic bird comes all the time, he can occasionally give you a ride," added the tortoise.

Stefan Little-Beak recognized the referee call of the red-billed tropicbird. The bird was on its way back to Daphne. Stefan had decided to depart.

"Thanks a lot for your help. I must leave now to help the Grants in understanding more about finches and evolution," and Stefan hitched a ride on the back of his tropicbird comrade.

He flew back to his important home island. He had met the tortoise that had met Darwin, and he was ready to explore his own great laboratory of evolution, Daphne Major.

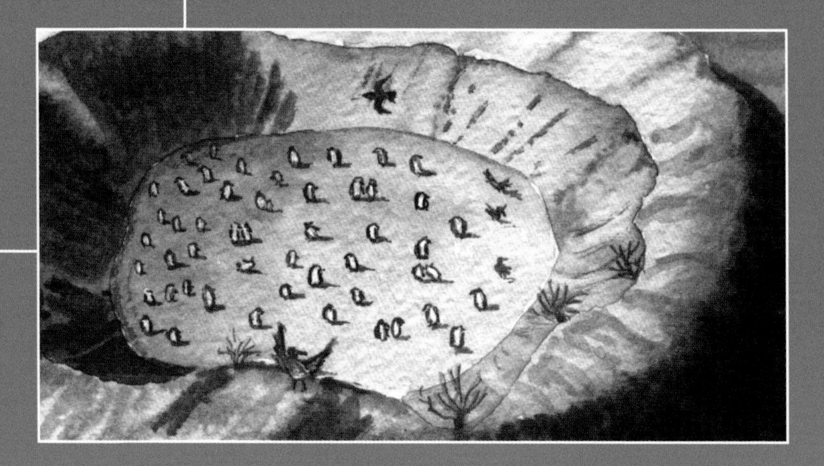

Verses about how some species colonized the Galápagos islands

Baltra bedtime story

(It can be made into a play as well.)

About the dispersal to the islands

TRANSPORTED BY SEA

Sea Lion

I came swimming from California,
It was not so difficult for me
A good swimmer I have always been.
A Californian I can no longer claim to be
Now endemic though I am,
I evolved for this very sea.

Penguin

Penguin, pingüino, penguin.
Anchovies, sardines, vanilla ice cream.
All I need I found in here
Because Humboldt and Cromwell are so very near.
Both sea currents feel really cold,
No other penguins so north have come or been so bold.

Marine iguana

My grandmother told me
That Great-grand mother told her
That a hitchhiker she was
And on a raft she arrived.
Many hippie creatures joined in,
Those that resisted heat and salt,
Such as insects, little rats and moths,
Here we adapted to a fault!

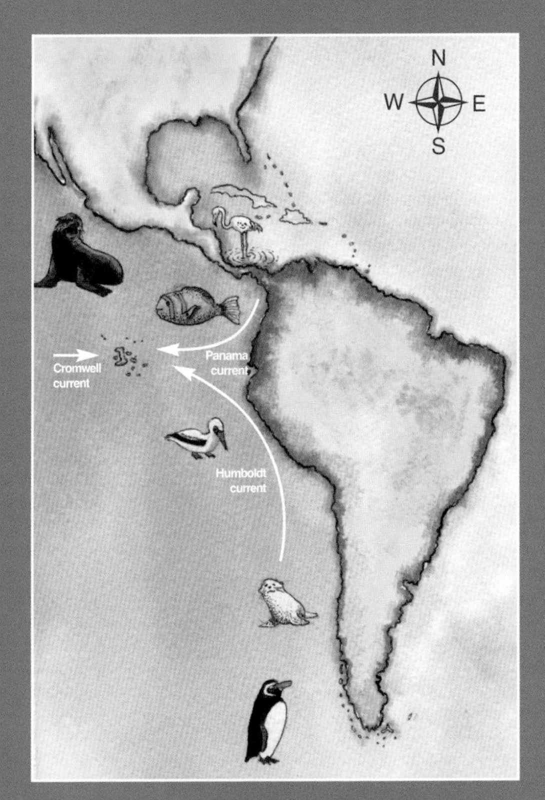

Carpenter Bee

A carpenter bee am I
Who loves yellow flowers, oh my!
I live in the trees
Have buzzed many weeks.
On a raft I came,
And no-one to blame.

Tortoise

I am a tortoise, not a sea turtle
I do walk, but I can't do the hurdle.
The question is this:
How did I get to this island of bliss?
Since I can't swim, sail a boat, but can float.

TRANSPORTED BY AIR

Mockingbird

Far flying is not for me,
Only four in my family tree
To Galápagos I came wind-blown
Now I stick to my island home.

Fern

My light spores arrived by air
To the cool wet zone up there.
Over a hundred species became we,
Living on soil, rock and tree.

Sea birds (Pelicans, Frigates, Terns and Petrels)

To fly for us is not a risk
Especially when the wind is brisk.
We fly between shore and sea
Mainland or island wherever we be
So endemic we are not
To fly free all over is our lot.

Frigatebird

A randy male frigate
Is not an easy bird to be,
Perching on the branches
And waiting for chicks to come to me.

Swallow-tailed Gull

Swallow-tailed gull am I
I like to go out at night.
Come and watch me in the dark sky
Because I stand out, I am white!

Blue-footed Booby

We are Blue-footed boobies
The ones you like to see
Watch us dance with our blue feet
And clowns we seem to be.

Red-footed booby

Further than "blues" I fly
Therefore pelagic am I.

Nazca booby

Siblicide, my chicks always do.
The oldest against the youngest
And only one will make it through.
Masked or Nazca, my looks, like them do you?

TRANSPORTED BY BIRDS

Mr. Seed

The way I got here
Is a little embarrassing to explain.
A bird ate me on the mainland, and then...
Just guess from where I came!

About the establishment

Hummingbird

To Galápagos I came
Wasn't hard to arrive
But red flowers I did not find
So I shall therefore die, no more of my kind!

Orchid

We orchids live up on high,
But need our fungal friends to get by
And he is a fungus
And lives right among us!

Fungus

The orchid might have arrived
But for us the fungi it's much harder to fly.
With just a few of us around
Only some orchids grew up, by and by.

Mr. Establishment

Alive, we arrive
No competitors,
Few predators
And many things to eat.
For those who survive,
Life really is a treat!

GLOSSARY

Adaptive radiation: it is the change from one single ancestor, animal or plant, into several kinds, each of them occupying a different environment.

Alga: common name for a simple type of plant that can be found in most environments on Earth, although the majority occur in freshwater or marine environments.

Apterous: means without wings (from the Greek a, not, and pteron, wing).

Archipelago: group of islands.

Ash: fine particles of lava thrown out by an erupting volcano.

Bioluminescence: light produced by living organisms.

Calamari: name for cooked and ready to eat squid.

Caldera: large volcanic depression or crater, that has been enlarged through erosion, sinking, or violent explosion.

Cinder cone: volcanic cone built of material dominated by fragments ranging from as tiny as grains of sand, to the size of pebbles (2-64 mm diameter).

Competition: interaction between individuals of the same species, or between different species populations, in which the growth and survival of one affects the survival and growth of the other.

Coral: marine creature, mostly colonial, with a skeleton that could be made of different materials (calcareous, horny or soft skeleton).

Crater: relatively small, funnel-shaped depression produced by eruptions.

Crustacean: a creature like crabs, lobsters, shrimps, woodlice and barnacles.

Darwin, Charles Robert: 1809-1882, English naturalist who is remembered mainly for his theory of evolution, which he based largely on observations made in 1832-36 during a voyage around the world on HMS Beagle, which was engaged on a mapping survey.

Endemic: plant or animal that is limited to one particular place, and found nowhere else in the world.

Extruded: material that has been ejected during an eruption.

Food-chain: transfer of energy from the green plants, through a series of organisms that eat and are eaten.

Garúa: local name for a fine mist formed in elevated areas of the Galápagos, usually between July and December.

Hot Spot: area with concentration of heat that never moves, and located deep within the Earth. That heat melts the rocks, which rise to the surface to form volcanoes.

Hybrid: individual plant or animal resulting from a cross between parents of different kinds. A good example is the mule, a hybrid between the horse and the donkey.

Interbreed: breed within a single family resulting in particular characteristics in the offspring.

Kleptoparasite: making a living from stealing from others.

Mangrove: salt tolerant forest developed in protected coves.

Metropolis: big city.

Natural Selection: complex process in which the total environment determines which members of a species survives to reproduce, and so pass on their characteristics to the next generation.

Lava: molten rock emitted by a volcano. Two varieties of lava surface are recognized: "aa", which shows a jagged, stony clinker, bristling with sharp points; and "pahohoe" characterized by a smooth, ropy appearance.

Octopus: creature with 8 long arms possessing suckers, and a round, sack-like body.

Parasitic cone: a volcanic cone forming on the flank of a larger volcano.

Pelagic: organisms of open ocean.

Pharyngeal jaws: jaws in the pharynx, which is the part of the gut that lies between the buccal cavity and the tube, called esophagus, which brings the food to the stomach.

Polyps: the soft-bodied part of coral, with a cylindrical trunk fixed at one end, with the mouth surrounded by tentacles at the other end.

Predator: creature that obtains energy (as food) by usually killing another, the prey.

Spatter cones: volcanic cone built from fragments blown out as clots of relatively fluid lava.

Species: group of organisms that resemble one another closely.

Tectonic plates: rigid blocks in which the outer most layer of the earth is divided in (the lithosphere) that are floating on semi molten rock (the astenosphere) and are able to interact with each other. Sometimes they collide, sometimes they move away from each other and sometimes they slide by each other.

Trade Winds: old maritime term for the winds blowing sideways towards the equator from the southeast, in the Southern Hemisphere.

Tuff: rock formed by compacted volcanic ash.